RAMADAN MADE EASY

WRITTEN AND ILLUSTRATED BY:
NAEEMAH S. CARSTON

COPYRIGHT

Ramadan Made Easy
(c)2025, Naeemah S. Carston
All rights reserved

Ramadan Made Easy-Author-Naeemah S. Carston

Portions (c) 2024, Naeemah S. Carston

No claim to copyright is made for original U.S. Government Works.

Copyright © 2026 by Naeemah Carston
All Rights Reserved by the author under U.S. copyright laws. This book may not be reproduced, in whole or in part, in any form without the written permission from the author.

Printed in the United States of America

On The Spelling of G-d
"We are not the first to make this change. To recognize the word dog in the reverse reading of the Name is distasteful. Many Jews agree. We favor such Jewish sentiments and share their concern ."
-Imam W. Deen Mohammed

DEDICATION TO
<u>IMAM DARNELL & GLORIA KARIM</u>

This book is dedicated to my beloved grandparents, Imam Darnell Karim and Sister Gloria Karim—pioneers, scholars, and lifelong servants of Al-Islam. Rising through the Nation of Islam and dedicating their lives to the spiritual and intellectual growth of the community. They have shaped generations through knowledge, discipline, and unwavering faith.Preserved in the African American Museum in Washington, D.C., my grandfather's voice—his recitation of the Adhan echoing through the exhibits—stands as a living testament to his impact.From weekly Jumu'ah khutbahs and Hafiz programs to lectures delivered across the world, his commitment to teaching Islam has left an enduring mark.

By his side, Sister Gloria Karim has been a constant source of wisdom, strength, and guidance—deeply rooted in the Qur'an and present in Arabic classes, Jumu'ah services, and community education. Together they have built a legacy of scholarship through countless books, recordings, and educational works centered on the history and practice of Al-Islam. This third volume of Ramadan Made Easy is an offering of gratitude and love, dedicated to honoring their legacy and ensuring it continues to live on through every generation that follows.

DEDICATION

To all the oppressed and marginalized communities around the world, may Allah ease your burdens and grant you strength in the face of adversity. During this blessed month of Ramadan and everyday. We pray for your peace, good health, freedom, and security. May you feel the mercy and justice of Allah, and may your struggles be met with relief and hope.

-Ameen

DEDICATION

This is dedicated to several family members who have inspired me to make this beautiful creation.

In loving memory of my Aunt Ayesha, whose wisdom and guidance taught me to always speak the truth and stand firm in what is right. Her influence shaped my life beyond what words can express, and her legacy continues to resonate.

To the love of my life who's been right by my side as I embark on my journey to get closer to Allah. I'm grateful for the late nights and early morning discussions regarding how to bring value to this work of art. I appreciate the dedicated support and I thank you for selflessly pushing me to be the best Naeemah I can be. We're a team and I couldn't have done it without you!

To my children...Aydin,Nahla,Noah and Adam. Remember to always be the best you can be, strive for excellence and never let up on your dreams. Most importantly be G'd fearing!

To my mom and dad, words can hardly describe the gratitude I have for you. You have been my source of inspiration, support, and guidance. You have taught me to be unique, determined, to believe in myself, and to always perservere. I am honored to have you as my parents.

To my baby sister, Aqeelah Karriem , who passed away May '23. May Allah forgive you of your sins and grant you Jannah tul firdus.I know you would be soo proud of the hard work and dedication that was put into this composition. Love you always!

PREFACE

My name is Naeemah Carston, a Muslim African American woman raised between Chicago, Illinois, and Atlanta, Georgia. I grew up in a home deeply in a home deeply grounded in faith, family, and community.I am fortunate to have been raised listening to influential leaders such as Imam Warith Deen Mohammed, during Eid celebrations with my grandparents at the Harvey Islamic Center. The love and support I have received from my family and the Atlanta Masjid Al-Islam community has helped shape my understanding of Islam and has contributed to strengthening my relationship with Allah.

Ramadan is a sacred time of reflection, discipline, and drawing closer to Allah. Ramadan Made Easy was created as a companion for this blessed month—designed to support prayer, organization, and intentional spiritual growth. In recent years, personal loss has deepened my reliance on Allah and reinforced the importance of structure, reflection, and faith during Ramadan. With the encouragement of my family this planner has become an essential part of my own Ramadan practice.

About This Edition
This updated edition includes:
- QR codes to duā' recitations by Sister Gloria Karim
- Curated duā's and sadaqah prompts for each set of ten days
- A simplified layout for tracking ṣalāh, gratitude, duā', and reflection
- New suḥūr and ifṭār recipes

May this book bring ease, barakah, and intention to your Ramadan. May Allah accept your worship and grant you a blessed month.

TABLE OF CONTENTS

DEDICATIONS
PREFACE
THE FIVE PILLARS OF ISLAM 1
WHAT IS RAMADAN? 2
THE OBLIGATION OF FASTING DURING RAMADAN...3
FREQUENTLY ASKED QUESTIONS 4
SUGGESTIONS FOR RAMADAN 8
EID AL-FITR 9
EXEMPTIONS FROM FASTING 10
RAMADAN 2026 GOALS 11
WUDU (ABLUTION) 12
THE FIVE DAILY PRAYERS 13
HOW THE FIVE DAILY PRAYERS BECAME OBLIGATORY 14
COMMONLY USED ISLAMIC TERMS 17
THE THREE PHASES OF RAMADAN 19
RAMADAN DAILY TRACKER (DAYS 1–30) 20
THE IMPORTANCE OF HYDRATION 50
SUHOOR RECIPES 51
IFTAR RECIPES 53
SURAH NOTES 55
DUAS FROM THE QUR'AN 59
NOTES 63

FIVE PILLARS OF ISLAM

SHAHADATAIN	SALAT	ZAKAT	SAWM	HAJJ
DECLARATION OF FAITH	OBLIGATORY PRAYERS	COMPULSORY GIVING	FASTING DURING RAMADAN	PILGRIMAGE TO MECCA

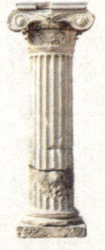   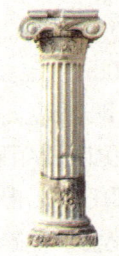 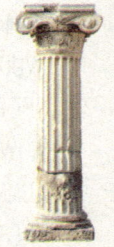

THE SHAHADA IS THE FOUNDATIONAL PRINCIPLE OF ISLAM AND IS CENTRAL TO A MUSLIM'S BELIEF.	THE RITUALISTIC DAILY PRAYER THAT MUSLIMS ARE REQUIRED TO PERFORM FIVE TIMES A DAY	A COMPULSORY ANNUAL DONATION OF 2.5% OF A MUSLIM'S NET WEALTH, GIVEN TO PURIFY WEALTH AND SUPPORT THE NEEDY.	RAMADAN IS THE HOLY MONTH OF FASTING, PRAYER, AND REFLECTION OBSERVED BY MUSLIMS TO STRENGTHEN FAITH AND SELF-DISCIPLINE.	HAJJ IS THE ANNUAL PILGRIMAGE TO MECCA, A ONCE-IN-A-LIFETIME OBLIGATION FOR ELIGIBLE MUSLIMS SYMBOLIZING UNITY, DEVOTION, AND SUBMISSION TO ALLAH.

WHAT IS RAMADAN?

The holy month of Ramadan is described as the return to Fitrah, your natural self. It is important to remember we are fasting for the sake of Allah (SWT).

Ramadan is the month in which the Qur'an was revealed to the Prophet Muhammad (PBUH). During this holy month, Muslims around the world fast from dawn to dusk (before sunrise and immediately after sunset). Fasting is a private act of worship that brings nearness to Allah (G'd), spiritual discipline, and empathy for those less fortunate.

Fasting is compulsory for those who are mentally and physically fit, past the age of puberty, in a settled situation (not traveling 50 miles or more), and are sure fasting is unlikely to cause real physical or mental injury.

2:183
ye who believe! may (learn) self-restraint Fasting is prescribed to you as it was prescribed to those before you, that ye may (learn) self-restraint.

2:185
Ramadan is the (month) in which was sent down the Qur'an, as a guide to mankind, also clear (Signs) for guidance and judgment (Between right and wrong). So every one of you who is present (at his home) during that month should spend it in fasting, but if any one is ill, or on a journey, the prescribed period (Should be made up) by days later. Allah intends every facility for you; He does not want to put you to difficulties. (He wants you) to complete the prescribed period, and to glorify Him in that He has guided you; and perchance
ye shall be grateful.
:

THE OBLIGATION OF FASTING DURING RAMADAN

Q: How Did Fasting During Ramadan Become Obligatory in Islam?
A: The revelations from G-d to the Prophet Muhammad that would eventually become compiled as the Qur'an began during Ramadan in the year 610 AD in Saudi Arabia. The obligation to fast is explained in the second chapter of the Qur'an. 'O ye who believe! Fasting is prescribed to you as it was prescribed to those before you, that ye may (leam) self-restraint. Ramadan is the (month) in which was sent down the Qur'an as a guide to mankind; also clear (Signs) for guidance and judgment (between right and wrong). So everyone of you who is present (at his home) during that month should spend it in fasting...'
(Chapter 2, verses 183 and 185.)

Q: What do Muslims believe they gain from fasting?
A: The main benefits of Ramadan are an increased compassion for those in need of the necessities of life, a sense of self-purification and reflection, and a renewed focus on spirituality.
Muslims also appreciate the feeling of togetherness shared by family and friends throughout the month. Perhaps the greatest practical benefit is the yearly lesson in self-restraint and discipline that can carry forward to other aspects of a Muslim's life such as work and education.

FREQUENTLY ASKED QUESTIONS

Q: What do you mean by observation of fasts?
A. By observation of fasts I mean the act of abstaining from eating, drinking, smoking, or allowing anything whatsoever to enter into what is understood to be the interior of the dawn till sunset.body, as also voluntary vomiting, self-pollution, sexual intercourse, etc.

Q: Who should fast during Ramadan?
A. The observation of fasts is obligatory on all Muslims excepting the infants, the insane, and the invalid.

Q. Why is the observation of fasts obligatory during the month of Ramadan?
A. The observation of fasts is obligatory in the month of Ramadan because it is the blessed month of the year during which the Holy Qur'an was revealed.

Q. Can we spread out the period of fasting and complete the observation of fasts from the required number of days - 29 or 30, as the case may be - at any time during the year?
A: No. The Holy Qur'an enjoins upon Muslims to observe the fasts consecutively for 29 or 30 days, as the case may be, during the month of Ramadan alone. Besides, the main purpose for which the observation of fasts has been made obligatory will not be served if the period were spread out, for the training that one receives for bearing with thirst and hunger, and incidentally realizing the distress of the starving poor and sympathizing with and helping them would be acquired.

FREQUENTLY ASKED QUESTIONS

Q: What is the real significance of fasting?
A: The true significance of fasting lies in the self-discipline it cultivates, helping a person resist temptation and reduce the likelihood of sin. This practice of restraint not only makes it easier to embrace virtue but also draws one closer to the Kingdom of Allah.

Q: What should be done if one does not observe a fast without any cogent reason on any day during the month of Ramadan?
A: If one does not fast on any day during the month of Ramadan without any cogent reason, chances of committing a sin, but all the same he or she must fast on some other day to make amends for the omission.

Q. What are the main obligatory factors for the proper observation of fasts?
A. The main obligatory factors for the proper observation of fasts are:
(1) Conception or utterance of Niyyah, i.e., intention to fast.
(2) Abstinence from all things that nullify the fast from the break of dawn to sunset.

Q: Is it permissible to fast voluntarily outside of Ramadan?
A: Voluntary fasting is permitted throughout the year as an act of worship and spiritual discipline. Muslims may choose to fast on days outside of Ramadan to seek closeness to Allah and increase reward. However, fasting is not permitted on the two days of Eid, which are designated for celebration and gratitude.

FREQUENTLY ASKED QUESTIONS

Q: What is the usual form of Niyyah for fasting during the month of Ramadan?
A: The usual form of Niyyah for fasting the month of Ramadan is:
Eating Suhoor (meal before the fast begins)
I intend to fast for this day in order to perform my duty towards Allah in the month of Ramadan of the present year.

Q: When should one conceive the Niyyat or give utterance to it?
A. The Niyyat (i.e., the intention) should be conceived or given utterance to for each day preferably before the break of dawn, if not, at any time before midday, if in the meanwhile one has maintained the state of fasting from the time of dawn.

Q. What are the main optional for the observation of fast?
A. The recommended practices for observing fasts include:
- Partaking of meals before the break of dawn.
- Reciting, prior to breaking the fast, the du'a:I.e., "Oh Allah For thy sake have I fasted and (now) I break the fast with the food that comes from Thee!"
- Eating of dates/natural fruits and drinking of water after sunset for signifying the end of the fast.
- Make Maghrib Prayer
- Eating of Iftar Dinner

FREQUENTLY ASKED QUESTIONS

Q: Why does Ramadan begin on a different day each year?
A: Because Ramadan is a lunar month, it begins about eleven days earlier each year. Throughout a Muslim's lifetime, Ramadan will fall both during winter months, when the days are short, and summer months, when the days are long and the fast is more difficult. This way, the difficulty of the fast is evenly distributed between Muslims living in the northern and southern hemispheres.

Q: What is LAILAT uL-QADR (NIGHT OF POWER)?
A: Laila-tul-Qadr (Night of Power) marks the anniversary of the night on which the Prophet Muhammad (PBUH) first began receiving revelations from G-d, through the angel Gabriel. An entire chapter in the Qur'an deals with this night: We have indeed revealed this (Message) in the Night of Majesty - and what will explain to thee what the Night of Majesty is? The Night of Majesty is better than a thousand months. Therein come down the angels and the Spirit by G-d's permission, on every errand. Peace. This until the rise of morn.' (Chapter 97) Muslims believe Laila-tul-Qadr is one of the last odd-numbered nights of Ramadan.

SUGGESTIONS DURING RAMADAN

1. Read the Qur'an daily — even a few verses bring light to the heart.
2. Pray your Sunnah prayers before or after Salah — consistency builds closeness.
3. Increase your remembrance (Dhikr) — let your tongue stay busy with gratitude.
4. Give charity often — time, words and or wealth; all count in the sight of Allah.
5. Control your tongue and temper — fasting is more than abstaining from food.
6. Reconnect with family or visit someone who's ill — small presence, big reward.
7. Feed someone at iftar — even dates and water carry immense reward.
8. Seek forgiveness daily — for yourself and believers everywhere.
9. Spend time in the masjid — attend a lecture or prayer beyond the obligatory.
10. Perform Taraweeh prayers, the nightly Ramadan prayers after Isha, to nurture faith and support the community.
11. Provide Iftar meals to support those observing the fast and strengthen the community.
12. Reflect and prepare for Laylat al-Qadr (Night of Power) — make dua with a full heart.

EID-AL-FITR
("FESTIVAL OF BREAKING FAST")

Eid-al-Fitr ("Festival of Fast Breaking")
Prayers at the End of Ramadan

- Eid begins with special morning prayers on the first day of Shawwal, the month following Ramadan on the Islamic lunar calendar, and lasts for three days.

- It is forbidden to fast during Eid because it is a time for relaxation.

- During Eid Muslims greet each other with the phrase "Eid Mubarak"(eed-moo-bar-ak); meaning 'blessed Eid."

- During Eid-al-Fitr, Muslims around the world dress in their finest attire and gather over large meals with family and friends.

- Zakat Al-Fitr is a form of Eid tax that has to be paid by the end of Ramadan. It should be distributed to the poor and needy in time for them to celebrate on the day of Eid.

EXCEPTIONS FROM FASTING

ALLAH DOES NOT BURDEN A SOUL BEYOND THAT IT CAN BEAR." — QUR'AN 2:286

- CHILDREN: THOSE WHO HAVE NOT YET REACHED PUBERTY.
- ELDERLY: WHEN FASTING CAUSES WEAKNESS OR HARDSHIP.
- PREGNANT OR BREASTFEEDING WOMEN: IF FASTING MAY HARM THE MOTHER OR CHILD.
- TRAVELERS: THOSE ON A JOURNEY THAT BRINGS DIFFICULTY.
- TEMPORARILY ILL: MAY MAKE UP MISSED FASTS LATER.
- CHRONICALLY ILL: EXEMPT; GIVE FIDYAH (FEED ONE PERSON PER MISSED DAY).
- WOMEN DURING MENSTRUATION OR POSTPARTUM BLEEDING:
- MENTALLY INCAPACITATED: NOT ACCOUNTABLE FOR FASTING.

RAMADAN 2026 GOALS

1. _____

2. _____

3. _____

4. _____

5. _____

6. _____

PURIFICATION IN ISLAM: WUDU, GHUSL, AND TAYAMMLUM

Wudu is a physical and spiritual act of purification, symbolizing inner and outer cleanliness.

Wudu is required for a valid prayer, as confirmed by the Prophet Muhammad (peace be upon him).

Minor ritual impurities that break wudu include urination, defecation passing gas, deep sleep, lustful emission of Pre, Seminole, fluid intoxication or a state of insanity or loss of consciousness. Wudu is broken by these substances: pus, pre-seminal fluid, semen, blood, urine, and feces.

After using the restroom, it is important to perform istinja (the act of cleaning with water not just wiping with tissue). Wudu is required to be performed again if any of these actions or substances are a factor.

Wudu is an Islamic ritual of partial, or minor, ablution performed before prayer to achieve physical and spiritual purity.

Make a supplication: It is recommended to say a prayer after completing the wudu.

WUDU (ABLUTION)
1. MAKE NIYYAH AND SAY BISMILLAH.
2. WASH HANDS 3 TIMES (RIGHT FIRST).
3. RINSE MOUTH 3 TIMES.
4. CLEAN NOSE 3 TIMES.
5. WASH FACE 3 TIMES.
6. WASH ARMS TO ELBOWS 3 TIMES (RIGHT FIRST).
7. WIPE HEAD AND EARS 1 TIME.
8. WASH FEET TO ANKLES 3 TIMES (RIGHT FIRST).

GHUSL
(FULL BODY PURIFICATION)
1. MAKE NIYYAH AND SAY BISMILLAH.
2. WASH HANDS AND PRIVATE AREAS.
3. PERFORM WUDU.
4. POUR WATER OVER THE ENTIRE BODY 1 TIME, ENSURING FULL COVERAGE.

TAYAMMUM (DRY ABLUTION)
1. MAKE NIYYAH AND SAY BISMILLAH.
2. TOUCH CLEAN EARTH WITH BOTH HANDS.
3. WIPE FACE 1 TIME.
4. TOUCH CLEAN EARTH AGAIN AND WIPE HANDS TO WRISTS 1 TIME.

A dry ablution called **tayammum** can be used if water is not available or if it would be harmful.

5 DAILY PRAYERS

The salah is a special form of worship that is the second pillar of Islam after the shahada (testimony of faith). It is an obligatory form of prayer performed five times a day that was revealed in the Holy Qur'an and taught to us by Prophet Muhammad (peace be upon him).
There are many verses in the Holy Quran which Allah tells us about the importance of prayer. Here are two such verses:

Why do Muslims Pray Salah?
The reason why Muslims pray at all relates to what Islam considers to be the purpose of life – to worship Allah alone. Shortly after Muhammad became a Prophet the performance of salah (worship) was one of the first commandments given to him by Allah.
Allah Almighty tells us in the Holy Qur'an that mankind was only created for one reason: to worship Him.

One of the biggest differences between a Muslim and a non-Muslim is the salah. Our beloved Prophet (peace be upon him) said:
"Between a man and polytheism and disbelief there stands his neglect of the prayer."

HOW DID THE 5 PRAYERS BECOME OBLIGATORY?

This question is quite common and many people do not know the real reason of where the number five came from. When Muhammad (peace be upon him) became a Prophet at the age of forty one of the first things he was taught was how to pray. Allah sent the angel Gabriel (Jibreel) to teach him how to make wudu and perform the salah.

Some 11 years after the beginning of prophethood a miraculous journey took place in which the angel Gabriel took Muhammad (peace be upon him) to the first heaven. It was during this event that Allah commanded him and the Muslims to specifically pray five times a day. This event was recorded in the Holy Qur'an and we also have authentic narrations from the Prophet (peace be upon him) himself that he undertook this journey.

The full story of the Prophet's ascent to heaven is known as Isra and Mi'raj. It is a lengthy story for which we will not go into detail. However, the last part of the story will be shared; the part where the commandment to pray specifically five times a day was given. Up until that point in history the Muslims would perform salah, but there was no specific number of times that was legislated.

The Story of Isra and Mi'raj

Exalted is He who took His Servant (Prophet Muhammad) by night from al-Masjid al-Haram (In Makkah) to al-Masjid al- Aqsa (Jerusalem), whose surroundings We have blessed, to show him of Our signs. Indeed, He is the Hearing, the Seeing. Qur'an - Chapter 17, Verse 1

The last part of the Isra and Mi'raj story begins at the moment the angel Gabriel (Jibreel) brings Muhammad (peace be upon him) from Makkah to Jerusalem, and then to the gates of the first level of heaven:

HOW DID THE 5 PRAYERS BECOME OBLIGATORY?

When I reached the nearest heaven. Gabriel said to the heaven gatekeeper, 'Open the gate.' The gatekeeper asked, 'Who is it?' He said, 'Gabriel.' The gatekeeper asked,' Who is accompanying you?' Gabriel said, 'Muhammad.' The gatekeeper said, 'Has he been called?' Gabriel said, 'Yes.' Then it was said, 'He is welcomed. What a wonderful visit his is!' Then I met Adam and greeted him and he said,
'You are welcomed O son and Prophet.'

Then we ascended to the second heaven. It was asked, 'Who is it?' Gabriel said, 'Gabriel.' It was said, 'Who is with you?' He said, 'Muhammad.' It was asked, 'Has he been sent for?' He said, 'Yes.' It was said, 'He is welcomed. What a wonderful visit his is!" Then I met Isa (Jesus) and Yahya (John the Baptist) who said, 'You are welcomed, O brother and a Prophet.'

Then we ascended to the third heaven. It was asked, 'Who is it?' Gabriel said, 'Gabriel.' It was asked, 'Who is with you? Gabriel said, 'Muhammad.' It was asked, 'Has he been sent for?' 'Yes,' said Gabriel. 'He is welcomed. What a wonderful visit his is!' (The Prophet added:). There I met Joseph (Yusuf) and greeted him, and he replied, 'You are welcomed, O brother and a Prophet!'

Then we ascended to the 4th heaven and again the same questions and answers were exchanged as in the previous heavens. There I met Idris and greeted him. He said, 'You are welcomed O brother and Prophet.'

Then we ascended to the 5th heaven and again the same questions and answers were exchanged as in previous heavens. There I met and greeted Aaron (Harun) who said,
'You are welcomed O brother and a Prophet".

HOW DID THE 5 PRAYERS BECOME OBLIGATORY?

Then we ascended to the 6th heaven and again the same questions and answers were exchanged as in the previous heavens. There I met and greeted Moses (Musa) who said, 'You are welcomed O brother and a Prophet.' When I proceeded on, he started weeping and on being asked why he was weeping, he said, 'O Lord! Followers of this youth who was sent after me will enter Paradise in great numbers than my followers.'

Then we ascended to the seventh heaven and again the same questions and answers were exchanged as in the previous heavens. There I met and greeted Abraham who said, 'You are welcomed O son and a Prophet.' Then I was shown al-Bait al-Ma'mur (i.e. God's House). I asked Gabriel about it and he said, This is al-Bait al-Ma'mur where 70,000 angels perform prayers daily and when they leave they never return to it (but always a new group comes into it daily).'
Then I was shown Sidrat al-Muntaha (i.e. a tree in the seventh heaven) and I saw its Nabk fruits which resembled the clay jugs of Hajr (i.e. a town in Arabia), and its leaves were like the ears of elephants, and four rivers originated at its root, two of them were apparent and two were hidden. I asked Gabriel about those rivers and he said, 'The two hidden rivers are in Paradise, and the apparent ones are the Nile and the Euphrates.'

Then fifty prayers were enjoined on me. I descended till I met Moses who asked me, 'What have you done?' I said, 'Fifty prayers have been enjoined on me.' He said, 'I know the people better than you, because I had the hardest experience to bring the Israelites to obedience. Your followers cannot put up with such obligation. So, return to your Lord and ask Him (to reduce the number of prayers).' I returned and asked Allah (for reduction) and He made it forty. I returned and (met Moses) and had a similar discussion, and then returned again to Allah for reduction and He made it thirty, then twenty, then ten, and then I came to Moses who repeated the same advice. Ultimately Allah reduced it to five. When I came to Moses again, he said, 'What have you done?' I said, 'Allah has made it five only.' He repeated the same advice but I said that I surrendered (to God's Final Order)'" God's Apostle was addressed by Allah, "I have decreed My Obligation and have reduced the burden on My servants, and I shall reward a single good deed as if it were ten good deeds.
— Sahih al-Bukhari, volume 4, Book 54, Hadith number 429

COMMONLY USED TERMS

ISLAM:
RELIGION OF COMPLETE SUBMISSION AND OBEDIENCE TO ALLAH.

MUSLIM:
SOMEONE WHO SUBMITS TO G'D AND LIVES IN ACCORDANCE WITH G'D'S WILL.

LAILA-TUL-QADR:
NIGHT OF POWER

TARAWEEH:
NIGHTLY PRAYERS

IFTAR:
FAST-BREAKING MEAL

SALAH:
DAILY RITUAL PRAYER

SAWM:
FASTING

SUHOOR:
PRE-FASTING MEAL

ZAKAT AL-FITR:
CHARITY

EID AL-FITR:
FAST-BREAKING FESTIVAL

WITR:
PRAYER

SUNSET:
IFTAR

RAMADAN MUBARAK:
BLESSED RAMADAN

EID MUBARAK:
BLESSED EID CELEBRATION

TAKBIR EID:
SAID BEFORE YOU PRAY AT EID
G-D IS GREATER

COMMONLY USED TERMS

EID MUBARAK:
BLESSED EID CELEBRATION

SADAQAH:
CHARITY BEFORE PRAYING

SUNNAH PRAYER:
-2 STEPS

TAJWEED:
QUR'AN RECITATION

HAAFITH:
ONE MEMORIZES THE QUR'AN
(THAT LEADS TARAWEEH PRAYERS)

TAQWAH:
G-D CONSCIENCE

ITIKAAF:
SPIRITUAL RETREAT OPTIONAL

TASLEEM :
LOOK OVER YOUR RIGHT SHOULDER AND RECITE AS-SALAMU ALAYKUM WA RAHMATULLAH (PEACE AND BLESSINGS OF ALLAH BE UPON YOU)THEN REPEAT OVER YOUR LEFT

FAJR:
DAWN PRAYER

THUHR:
EARLY AFTERNOON PRAYER

ASR:
LATE AFTERNOON PRAYER

MAGHRIB:
SUNSET PRAYER

ISHA:
NIGHT PRAYER

QUR'AN:
THE CENTRAL HOLY BOOK OF ISLAM

THE THREE PHASES OF RAMADAN

Ramadan is a month of mercy, forgiveness, and salvation. While Allah's blessings are available throughout the entire month, these three phases serve as a guide to help focus intentions and deepen worship.

First Ten Days
Mercy (Raḥmah)
A time to renew intentions, soften the heart, and seek Allah's compassion.
Focus: Gratitude · Consistency · Humility

Second Ten Days
Forgiveness (Maghfirah)
A time for repentance, self-reflection, and seeking forgiveness from Allah and others.
Focus: Repentance · Patience · Personal Growth

Last Ten Days
Salvation ('Itq min an-Nār)
A time of increased worship, seeking protection from the Hellfire, and striving for Laylat al-Qadr.
Focus: Duʿā' · Night Prayer · Qur'an

Day 1

DATE :_____

🌙 **FAITH CHECKLIST**

SALAH   FAJR ☐   DHUHR ☐   ASR ☐   MAHGRIB ☐   ISHA ☐

DHIKR   MORNING ☐   EVENING ☐

QURAN   JUZ____   OPTIONAL: TARAWIH(تراويح) ☐

❤️ **GRATITUDE & FAMILY**

I'm grateful for: _____

Family moment or reflection: _____

🤲 **SADAQAH PROMPT:** Feed someone—at home, work, or a stranger.

TODAY I GAVE:_____

TIME ☐   SMILE ☐   FOOD ☐   SUPPORT ☐

🤲 **DUA AND REFLECTION:**

MY PERSONAL DUA:_____

Scan to hear dua resuscitation from Sister Gloria Karim!

O ALLAH, ACCEPT OUR FASTING AND PRAYERS, PLACE BARAKAH IN OUR EFFORTS, AND KEEP US CLOSE TO YOU. AMEEN.

Day 2

DATE: _____

🌙 FAITH CHECKLIST

SALAH FAJR ☐ DHUHR ☐ ASR ☐ MAHGRIB ☐ ISHA ☐

DHIKR MORNING ☐ EVENING ☐

QURAN JUZ ____ OPTIONAL: TARAWIH (تراويح) ☐

❤️ GRATITUDE & FAMILY

I'm grateful for: _____

Family moment or reflection: _____

SADAQAH PROMPT:
Send a kind, encouraging message to someone who may need it.

TODAY I GAVE: _____

TIME ☐   SMILE ☐   FOOD ☐   SUPPORT ☐

🤲 DUA AND REFLECTION:

MY PERSONAL DUA: _____

Scan to hear dua resuscitation from Sister Glorial Karim!

Day 3

DATE :_____

🌙 **FAITH CHECKLIST**

SALAH   FAJR ☐   DHUHR ☐   ASR ☐   MAHGRIB ☐   ISHA ☐

DHIKR   MORNING ☐   EVENING ☐

QURAN   JUZ____   OPTIONAL: TARAWIH (تراويح) ☐

❤️ **GRATITUDE & FAMILY**

I'm grateful for: _____

Family moment or reflection: _____

SADAQAH PROMPT: Make du'ā' for someone without telling them.

TODAY I GAVE:_____

TIME ☐   SMILE ☐   FOOD ☐   SUPPORT ☐

🤲 **DUA AND REFLECTION:**

MY PERSONAL DUA:_____

Scan to hear dua resuscitation from Sister Gloria Karim!

O ALLAH, ACCEPT OUR FASTING AND PRAYERS, PLACE BARAKAH IN OUR EFFORTS, AND KEEP US CLOSE TO YOU. AMEEN.

Day 4

DATE: _____

🌙 FAITH CHECKLIST

SALAH   FAJR ☐   DHUHR ☐   ASR ☐   MAHGRIB ☐   ISHA ☐

DHIKR   MORNING ☐   EVENING ☐

QURAN   JUZ ____   OPTIONAL: TARAWIH (تراويح) ☐

❤️ GRATITUDE & FAMILY

I'm grateful for: _____

Family moment or reflection: _____

🤲 SADAQAH PROMPT: Tip extra (barista, delivery, server).

TODAY I GAVE: _____

TIME ☐   SMILE ☐   FOOD ☐   SUPPORT ☐

🤲 DUA AND REFLECTION:

MY PERSONAL DUA: _____

Scan to hear dua resuscitation from Sister Gloria Karim!

O ALLAH, ACCEPT OUR FASTING AND PRAYERS, PLACE BARAKAH IN OUR EFFORTS, AND KEEP US CLOSE TO YOU. AMEEN.

Day 5

DATE :_____

FAITH CHECKLIST

SALAH FAJR ☐ DHUHR ☐ ASR ☐ MAHGRIB ☐ ISHA ☐

DHIKR MORNING ☐   EVENING ☐

QURAN JUZ____ OPTIONAL: TARAWIH (تراويح) ☐

GRATITUDE & FAMILY

I'm grateful for: _____

Family moment or reflection: _____

SADAQAH PROMPT: Share food with a neighbor.

TODAY I GAVE: _____

TIME ☐   SMILE ☐   FOOD ☐   SUPPORT ☐

DUA AND REFLECTION:

MY PERSONAL DUA: _____

Scan to hear dua resuscitation from Sister Gloria Karim!

Day 6

DATE :_____

🌙 FAITH CHECKLIST

SALAH   FAJR ☐   DHUHR ☐   ASR ☐   MAHGRIB ☐   ISHA ☐

DHIKR   MORNING ☐   EVENING ☐

QURAN   JUZ____   OPTIONAL: TARAWIH(تراويح) ☐

❤️ GRATITUDE & FAMILY

I'm grateful for: _____

Family moment or reflection: _____

🫴 SADAQAH PROMPT: Help someone with a task without being asked.

TODAY I GAVE:_____

TIME ☐   SMILE ☐   FOOD ☐   SUPPORT ☐

🤲 DUA AND REFLECTION:

MY PERSONAL DUA:_____

Scan to hear dua resuscitation from Sister Gloria Karim!

O ALLAH, ACCEPT OUR FASTING AND PRAYERS, PLACE BARAKAH IN OUR EFFORTS, AND KEEP US CLOSE TO YOU. AMEEN.

Day 7

DATE :_____

🌙 **FAITH CHECKLIST**

SALAH FAJR ☐ DHUHR ☐ ASR ☐ MAHGRIB ☐ ISHA ☐

DHIKR MORNING ☐ EVENING ☐

QURAN JUZ____ OPTIONAL: TARAWIH(تراويح) ☐

❤️ **GRATITUDE & FAMILY**

I'm grateful for: _____

Family moment or reflection: _____

🤲 **SADAQAH PROMPT:** Smile and greet others intentionally.

TODAY I GAVE:_____

TIME ☐   SMILE ☐   FOOD ☐   SUPPORT ☐

🤲 **DUA AND REFLECTION:**

MY PERSONAL DUA:_____

Scan to hear dua resuscitation from Sister Gloria Karim!

O ALLAH, ACCEPT OUR FASTING AND PRAYERS, PLACE BARAKAH IN OUR EFFORTS, AND KEEP US CLOSE TO YOU. AMEEN.

Day 8

DATE : _____

🌙 **FAITH CHECKLIST**

SALAH   FAJR ☐   DHUHR ☐   ASR ☐   MAHGRIB ☐   ISHA ☐

DHIKR   MORNING ☐   EVENING ☐

QURAN   JUZ ____   OPTIONAL: TARAWIH(تراويح) ☐

❤️ **GRATITUDE & FAMILY**

I'm grateful for: _____

Family moment or reflection: _____

🤲 **SADAQAH PROMPT:**   Donate quietly, even a small amount.

TODAY I GAVE: _____

TIME ☐   SMILE ☐   FOOD ☐   SUPPORT ☐

🤲 **DUA AND REFLECTION:**

MY PERSONAL DUA: _____

- -

Scan to hear dua resuscitation from Sister Gloria Karim!

O ALLAH, ACCEPT OUR FASTING AND PRAYERS, PLACE BARAKAH IN OUR EFFORTS, AND KEEP US CLOSE TO YOU. AMEEN.

Day 9

DATE: _____

FAITH CHECKLIST

SALAH FAJR ☐ DHUHR ☐ ASR ☐ MAHGRIB ☐ ISHA ☐

DHIKR MORNING ☐ EVENING ☐

QURAN JUZ ____ OPTIONAL: TARAWIH (تراويح) ☐

GRATITUDE & FAMILY

I'm grateful for: _____

Family moment or reflection: _____

SADAQAH PROMPT: Be patient and gentle with someone difficult.

TODAY I GAVE: _____

TIME ☐   SMILE ☐   FOOD ☐   SUPPORT ☐

DUA AND REFLECTION:

MY PERSONAL DUA: _____

Scan to hear dua resuscitation from Sister Gloria Karim!

O ALLAH, ACCEPT OUR FASTING AND PRAYERS, PLACE BARAKAH IN OUR EFFORTS, AND KEEP US CLOSE TO YOU. AMEEN.

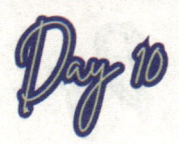

DATE : _____

FAITH CHECKLIST

SALAH   FAJR ☐   DHUHR ☐   ASR ☐   MAHGRIB ☐   ISHA ☐

DHIKR   MORNING _____   EVENING _____

QURAN   JUZ_____   OPTIONAL: TARAWIH(تراويح) ☐

GRATITUDE & FAMILY

I'm grateful for: _____

Family moment or reflection: _____

SADAQAH PROMPT: Forgive a small offense for the sake of Allah.

TODAY I GAVE: _____

TIME ☐   SMILE ☐   FOOD ☐   SUPPORT ☐

DUA AND REFLECTION:

MY PERSONAL DUA: _____

Scan to hear dua resuscitation from Sister Gloria Karim!

O ALLAH, ACCEPT OUR FASTING AND PRAYERS, PLACE BARAKAH IN OUR EFFORTS, AND KEEP US CLOSE TO YOU. AMEEN.

Day 11

DATE :_____

🌙 **FAITH CHECKLIST**

SALAH   FAJR ☐   DHUHR ☐   ASR ☐   MAHGRIB ☐   ISHA ☐

DHIKR   MORNING ☐   EVENING ☐

QURAN   JUZ____   OPTIONAL: TARAWIH(تراويح) ☐

❤️ **GRATITUDE & FAMILY**

I'm grateful for: _____
Family moment or reflection: _____

🤲 **SADAQAH PROMPT:** Ask forgiveness from someone you've hurt.

TODAY I GAVE:_____

TIME ☐   SMILE ☐   FOOD ☐   SUPPORT ☐

🤲 **DUA AND REFLECTION:**

MY PERSONAL DUA:_____

Scan to hear dua resuscitation from Sister Gloria Karim!

O ALLAH, FORGIVE US, HAVE MERCY ON US, AND STRENGTHEN OUR HEARTS IN WORSHIP. AMEEN

Day 12

DATE :_____

🌙 FAITH CHECKLIST

SALAH   FAJR ☐   DHUHR ☐   ASR ☐   MAHGRIB ☐   ISHA ☐

DHIKR   MORNING ☐   EVENING ☐

QURAN   JUZ____   OPTIONAL: TARAWIH(تراويح) ☐

❤️ GRATITUDE & FAMILY

I'm grateful for: _____

Family moment or reflection: _____

🤲 SADAQAH PROMPT: Let go of a grudge.

TODAY I GAVE:_____

TIME ☐   SMILE ☐   FOOD ☐   SUPPORT ☐

🤲 DUA AND REFLECTION:

MY PERSONAL DUA:_____

Scan to hear dua resuscitation from Sister Gloria Karim!

O ALLAH, FORGIVE US, HAVE MERCY ON US, AND STRENGTHEN OUR HEARTS IN WORSHIP. AMEEN

DATE :_____

🌙 FAITH CHECKLIST

SALAH   FAJR ☐   DHUHR ☐   ASR ☐   MAHGRIB ☐   ISHA ☐

DHIKR   MORNING ☐   EVENING ☐

QURAN   JUZ____   OPTIONAL: TARAWIH(تراويح) ☐

❤️ GRATITUDE & FAMILY

I'm grateful for: _____

Family moment or reflection: _____

🤲 SADAQAH PROMPT: Give charity with the intention of expiation.

TODAY I GAVE:_____

TIME ☐   SMILE ☐   FOOD ☐   SUPPORT ☐

🤲 DUA AND REFLECTION:

MY PERSONAL DUA:_____

_____

Scan to hear dua resuscitation from Sister Gloria Karim!

O ALLAH, FORGIVE US, HAVE MERCY ON US, AND STRENGTHEN OUR HEARTS IN WORSHIP. AMEEN

Day 19

DATE :_____

🌙 FAITH CHECKLIST

SALAH   FAJR ☐   DHUHR ☐   ASR ☐   MAHGRIB ☐   ISHA ☐

DHIKR   MORNING ☐   EVENING ☐

QURAN   JUZ____   OPTIONAL: TARAWIH(تراويح) ☐

❤️ GRATITUDE & FAMILY

I'm grateful for: _____

Family moment or reflection: _____

SADAQAH PROMPT: Apologize sincerely—even if it's uncomfortable.

TODAY I GAVE:_____

TIME ☐   SMILE ☐   FOOD ☐   SUPPORT ☐

DUA AND REFLECTION:

MY PERSONAL DUA:_____

Scan to hear dua resuscitation from Sister Gloria Karim!

Day 15

DATE: _____

🌙 FAITH CHECKLIST

SALAH   FAJR ☐   DHUHR ☐   ASR ☐   MAHGRIB ☐   ISHA ☐

DHIKR   MORNING ☐   EVENING ☐

QURAN   JUZ____   OPTIONAL: TARAWIH (تراويح) ☐

❤️ GRATITUDE & FAMILY

I'm grateful for: _____

Family moment or reflection: _____

🤲 SADAQAH PROMPT:

Donate in someone else's name.

TODAY I GAVE: _____

TIME ☐   SMILE ☐   FOOD ☐   SUPPORT ☐

🤲 DUA AND REFLECTION:

MY PERSONAL DUA: _____

Scan to hear dua resuscitation from Sister Gloria Karim!

O ALLAH, FORGIVE US, HAVE MERCY ON US, AND STRENGTHEN OUR HEARTS IN WORSHIP. AMEEN

Day 16

DATE : _____

🌙 **FAITH CHECKLIST**

SALAH   FAJR ☐   DHUHR ☐   ASR ☐   MAHGRIB ☐   ISHA ☐

DHIKR   MORNING ☐   EVENING ☐

QURAN   JUZ____   OPTIONAL: TARAWIH (تراويح) ☐

❤️ **GRATITUDE & FAMILY**

I'm grateful for: _____

Family moment or reflection: _____

🫴 **SADAQAH PROMPT:** Make du'ā' for those who wronged you.

TODAY I GAVE: _____

TIME ☐   SMILE ☐   FOOD ☐   SUPPORT ☐

🤲 **DUA AND REFLECTION:**

MY PERSONAL DUA: _____

Scan to hear dua resuscitation from Sister Gloria Karim!

O ALLAH, FORGIVE US, HAVE MERCY ON US, AND STRENGTHEN OUR HEARTS IN WORSHIP. AMEEN

Day 17

DATE : _____

🌙 FAITH CHECKLIST

SALAH   FAJR ☐   DHUHR ☐   ASR ☐   MAHGRIB ☐   ISHA ☐

DHIKR   MORNING ☐   EVENING ☐

QURAN   JUZ____   OPTIONAL: TARAWIH (تراويح) ☐

❤️ GRATITUDE & FAMILY

I'm grateful for: _____

Family moment or reflection: _____

🤲 SADAQAH PROMPT: _

Delete something negative (texts, thoughts, posts).

TODAY I GAVE: _____

TIME ☐   SMILE ☐   FOOD ☐   SUPPORT ☐

🤲 DUA AND REFLECTION:

MY PERSONAL DUA: _____

Scan to hear dua resuscitation from Sister Gloria Karim!

O ALLAH, FORGIVE US, HAVE MERCY ON US, AND STRENGTHEN OUR HEARTS IN WORSHIP. AMEEN

Day 18

DATE :_____

🌙 FAITH CHECKLIST

SALAH   FAJR ☐   DHUHR ☐   ASR ☐   MAHGRIB ☐   ISHA ☐

DHIKR   MORNING ☐   EVENING ☐

QURAN   JUZ____   OPTIONAL: TARAWIH (تراويح) ☐

❤️ GRATITUDE & FAMILY

I'm grateful for: _____

Family moment or reflection: _____

🤲 SADAQAH PROMPT: Cover someone's mistake instead of exposing it.

TODAY I GAVE: _____

TIME ☐   SMILE ☐   FOOD ☐   SUPPORT ☐

🙌 DUA AND REFLECTION:

MY PERSONAL DUA: _____

Scan to hear dua resuscitation from Sister Gloria Karim!

O ALLAH, FORGIVE US, HAVE MERCY ON US, AND STRENGTHEN OUR HEARTS IN WORSHIP. AMEEN

Day 19

DATE :_____

🌙 **FAITH CHECKLIST**

SALAH   FAJR ☐   DHUHR ☐   ASR ☐   MAHGRIB ☐   ISHA ☐

DHIKR   MORNING ☐   EVENING ☐

QURAN   JUZ____   OPTIONAL: TARAWIH(تراويح) ☐

❤️ **GRATITUDE & FAMILY**

I'm grateful for: _____

Family moment or reflection: _____

🤲 **SADAQAH PROMPT:**   Give time or service, not just money.

TODAY I GAVE:_____

TIME ☐   SMILE ☐   FOOD ☐   SUPPORT ☐

🤲 **DUA AND REFLECTION:**

MY PERSONAL DUA:_____

Scan to hear dua resuscitation from Sister Gloria Karim!

O ALLAH, FORGIVE US, HAVE MERCY ON US, AND STRENGTHEN OUR HEARTS IN WORSHIP. AMEEN

Day 20

DATE: _____

🌙 FAITH CHECKLIST

SALAH   FAJR ☐   DHUHR ☐   ASR ☐   MAHGRIB ☐   ISHA ☐

DHIKR   MORNING ☐   EVENING ☐

QURAN   JUZ____   OPTIONAL: TARAWIH (تراويح) ☐

❤️ GRATITUDE & FAMILY

I'm grateful for: _____

Family moment or reflection: _____

🤲 SADAQAH PROMPT:
Pray two extra rak'ahs seeking forgiveness for yourself and others.

TODAY I GAVE: _____

TIME ☐   SMILE ☐   FOOD ☐   SUPPORT ☐

🤲 DUA AND REFLECTION:

MY PERSONAL DUA: _____

Scan to hear dua resuscitation from Sister Gloria Karim!

O ALLAH, FORGIVE US, HAVE MERCY ON US, AND STRENGTHEN OUR HEARTS IN WORSHIP. AMEEN

Day 21

DATE :_____

🌙 FAITH CHECKLIST

SALAH   FAJR ☐   DHUHR ☐   ASR ☐   MAHGRIB ☐   ISHA ☐

DHIKR   MORNING ☐   EVENING ☐

QURAN   JUZ____   OPTIONAL: TARAWIH(تراويح) ☐

❤️ GRATITUDE & FAMILY

I'm grateful for: _____
Family moment or reflection: _____

🤲 SADAQAH PROMPT: Give charity every night, even if very small.

TODAY I GAVE:_____

TIME ☐   SMILE ☐   FOOD ☐   SUPPORT ☐

🤲 DUA AND REFLECTION:

MY PERSONAL DUA:_____

Scan to hear dua resuscitation from Sister Gloria Karim!

O ALLAH, ACCEPT FROM US AND DRAW US NEARER TO YOU. AMEEN.

Day 22

DATE: _____

🌙 **FAITH CHECKLIST**

SALAH   FAJR ☐   DHUHR ☐   ASR ☐   MAHGRIB ☐   ISHA ☐

DHIKR   MORNING ☐   EVENING ☐

QURAN   JUZ____   OPTIONAL: TARAWIH(تراويح) ☐

❤️ **GRATITUDE & FAMILY**

I'm grateful for: _____

Family moment or reflection: _____

🤲 **SADAQAH PROMPT:** Feed someone breaking fast.

TODAY I GAVE: _____

TIME ☐   SMILE ☐   FOOD ☐   SUPPORT ☐

🤲 **DUA AND REFLECTION:**

MY PERSONAL DUA: _____

Scan to hear dua resuscitation from Sister Gloria Karim!

O ALLAH, ACCEPT FROM US AND DRAW US NEARER TO YOU. AMEEN.

Day 23

DATE :_____

☾ FAITH CHECKLIST

SALAH FAJR ☐ DHUHR ☐ ASR ☐ MAHGRIB ☐ ISHA ☐

DHIKR MORNING ☐ EVENING ☐

QURAN JUZ____ OPTIONAL: TARAWIH (تراويح) ☐

♥ GRATITUDE & FAMILY

I'm grateful for: _____

Family moment or reflection: _____

SADAQAH PROMPT: Support a Masjid, food bank, or family in need.

TODAY I GAVE:_____

TIME ☐   SMILE ☐   FOOD ☐   SUPPORT ☐

DUA AND REFLECTION:

MY PERSONAL DUA:_____

Scan to hear dua resuscitation from Sister Gloria Karim!

O ALLAH, ACCEPT FROM US AND DRAW US NEARER TO YOU. AMEEN.

Day 24

DATE: _____

FAITH CHECKLIST

SALAH   FAJR ☐   DHUHR ☐   ASR ☐   MAHGRIB ☐   ISHA ☐

DHIKR   MORNING ☐   EVENING ☐

QURAN   JUZ ____   OPTIONAL: TARAWIH (تراويح) ☐

GRATITUDE & FAMILY

I'm grateful for: _____

Family moment or reflection: _____

SADAQAH PROMPT: Donate secretly—no one needs to know.

TODAY I GAVE: _____

TIME ☐   SMILE ☐   FOOD ☐   SUPPORT ☐

DUA AND REFLECTION:

MY PERSONAL DUA: _____

Scan to hear dua resuscitation from Sister Gloria Karim!

O ALLAH, ACCEPT FROM US AND DRAW US NEARER TO YOU. AMEEN.

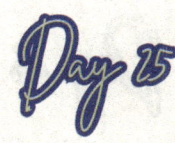

DATE :_____

FAITH CHECKLIST

SALAH FAJR ☐ DHUHR ☐ ASR ☐ MAHGRIB ☐ ISHA ☐

DHIKR MORNING ☐   EVENING ☐

QURAN JUZ____   OPTIONAL: TARAWIH(تراويح) ☐

GRATITUDE & FAMILY

I'm grateful for: _____

Family moment or reflection: _____

SADAQAH PROMPT: Wake for tahajjud and give charity after.

TODAY I GAVE: _____

TIME ☐   SMILE ☐   FOOD ☐   SUPPORT ☐

DUA AND REFLECTION:

MY PERSONAL DUA: _____

Scan to hear dua resuscitation from Sister Gloria Karim!

O ALLAH, ACCEPT FROM US AND DRAW US NEARER TO YOU. AMEEN.

Day 26

DATE: _____

🌙 **FAITH CHECKLIST**

SALAH   FAJR ☐   DHUHR ☐   ASR ☐   MAHGRIB ☐   ISHA ☐

DHIKR   MORNING ☐   EVENING ☐

QURAN   JUZ____   OPTIONAL: TARAWIH (تراويح) ☐

❤️ **GRATITUDE & FAMILY**

I'm grateful for: _____

Family moment or reflection: _____

🤲 **SADAQAH PROMPT:** Sponsor a meal, water, or essential item.

TODAY I GAVE: _____

TIME ☐   SMILE ☐   FOOD ☐   SUPPORT ☐

🤲 **DUA AND REFLECTION:**

MY PERSONAL DUA: _____

Scan to hear dua resuscitation from Sister Gloria Karim!

O ALLAH, ACCEPT FROM US AND DRAW US NEARER TO YOU. AMEEN.

Day 27

DATE :_____

🌙 FAITH CHECKLIST

SALAH   FAJR ☐   DHUHR ☐   ASR ☐   MAHGRIB ☐   ISHA ☐

DHIKR   MORNING ☐   EVENING ☐

QURAN   JUZ____   OPTIONAL: TARAWIH (تراويح) ☐

❤️ GRATITUDE & FAMILY

I'm grateful for: _____

Family moment or reflection: _____

🤲 SADAQAH PROMPT:

Give sadaqah with the intention of Laylat al-Qadr.

TODAY I GAVE: _____

TIME ☐   SMILE ☐   FOOD ☐   SUPPORT ☐

🤲 DUA AND REFLECTION:

MY PERSONAL DUA: _____

Scan to hear dua resuscitation from Sister Gloria Karim!

O ALLAH, ACCEPT FROM US AND DRAW US NEARER TO YOU. AMEEN.

Day 28

DATE: _____

🌙 FAITH CHECKLIST

SALAH   FAJR ☐   DHUHR ☐   ASR ☐   MAHGRIB ☐   ISHA ☐

DHIKR   MORNING ☐   EVENING ☐

QURAN   JUZ____   OPTIONAL: TARAWIH (تراويح) ☐

❤️ GRATITUDE & FAMILY

I'm grateful for: _____

Family moment or reflection: _____

🤲 SADAQAH PROMPT: Teach or share beneficial knowledge.

TODAY I GAVE: _____

TIME ☐   SMILE ☐   FOOD ☐   SUPPORT ☐

🤲 DUA AND REFLECTION:

MY PERSONAL DUA: _____

Scan to hear dua resuscitation from Sister Gloria Karim!

O ALLAH, ACCEPT FROM US AND DRAW US NEARER TO YOU. AMEEN.

Day 29

DATE :_____

☾ FAITH CHECKLIST

SALAH FAJR ☐ DHUHR ☐ ASR ☐ MAHGRIB ☐ ISHA ☐

DHIKR MORNING ☐ EVENING ☐

QURAN JUZ____ OPTIONAL: TARAWIH (تراويح) ☐

♥ GRATITUDE & FAMILY

I'm grateful for: _____

Family moment or reflection: _____

SADAQAH PROMPT:

Make duʿāʾ for the Ummah.

TODAY I GAVE: _____

TIME ☐   SMILE ☐   FOOD ☐   SUPPORT ☐

🤲 DUA AND REFLECTION:

MY PERSONAL DUA: _____

Scan to hear dua resuscitation from Sister Gloria Karim!

O ALLAH, ACCEPT FROM US AND DRAW US NEARER TO YOU. AMEEN.

Day 30

DATE :_____

FAITH CHECKLIST

SALAH   FAJR ☐   DHUHR ☐   ASR ☐   MAHGRIB ☐   ISHA ☐

DHIKR   MORNING ☐   EVENING ☐

QURAN   JUZ____   OPTIONAL: TARAWIH(تراويح) ☐

GRATITUDE & FAMILY

I'm grateful for: _____

Family moment or reflection: _____

SADAQAH PROMPT: Give your best charity in the last nights.

TODAY I GAVE:_____

TIME ☐   SMILE ☐   FOOD ☐   SUPPORT ☐

DUA AND REFLECTION:

MY PERSONAL DUA:_____

ONE THING I LEARNED OR WANT TO REMEMBER TOMORROW:

:_____

_____

Scan to hear dua resuscitation from Sister Gloria Karim!

O ALLAH, ACCEPT FROM US AND DRAW US NEARER TO YOU. AMEEN.

 # IMPORTANCE OF HYDRATION

- Suhoor (pre-dawn meal): Focus on drinking water and consuming foods with high water content like fruits (e.g., watermelon, oranges) and vegetables (e.g., cucumbers, tomatoes). Include hydrating foods like yogurt, soups, or oatmeal.

- Iftar (meal to break the fast): Start with water or an electrolyte-rich drink (like coconut water) to replenish fluids quickly. Afterward, continue drinking water between Iftar and bedtime.

Opt for foods that naturally contain water, such as fruits (e.g., cucumbers, strawberries, and oranges), vegetables, and salads. These not only hydrate but also provide essential vitamins and minerals..

Aim to drink 8-10 cups of water or fluids between Iftar and Suhoor. Spread this out to avoid overwhelming your stomach and to ensure constant hydration.

By focusing on water-rich foods and spacing out your fluid intake, you can help ensure that you stay hydrated throughout the month of Ramadan.

SUHOOR RECIPES

SAY: "I INTEND TO FAST FOR THIS DAY IN ORDER TO PERFORM MY DUTY TOWARDS ALLAH IN THE MONTH OF RAMADAN OF THE PRESENT YEAR."

BREAKFAST QUESADILLA
SCRAMBLED EGGS, SHREDDED CHEESE, RED ONION, BREAKFAST MEAT, TOMATO, SPINACH, WHOLE WHEAT TORTILLA
SCRAMBLE EGGS AND COOK WITH SPINACH, RED ONIONS, TOMATO AND YOUR CHOICE OF BREAKFAST MEAT, ADD SHREDDED CHEESE, WRAP IN A WARM WHOLE-WHEAT TORTILLA, AND SERVE.

BERRY ALMOND SMOOTHIE
ALMOND MILK, FROZEN BERRIES, ALMOND BUTTER
PROTEIN POWDER OR GREEK YOGURT
BLEND MIXED BERRIES, ALMOND MILK, AND ALMOND BUTTER UNTIL SMOOTH AND CREAMY; SERVE IMMEDIATELY.

BANANA NUT OVERNIGHT OATS
OATS, ALMOND MILK, BANANA, CHIA SEEDS, WALNUTS
COMBINE OATS, ALMOND MILK, MASHED BANANA, CHIA SEEDS, AND WALNUTS; REFRIGERATE OVERNIGHT AND ENJOY CHILLED OR SLIGHTLY WARMED.

SUHOOR RECIPES

SAY: "I INTEND TO FAST FOR THIS DAY IN ORDER TO PERFORM MY DUTY TOWARDS ALLAH IN THE MONTH OF RAMADAN OF THE PRESENT YEAR."

SWEET POTATO HASH
DICE SWEET POTATOES, BELL PEPPERS, ONIONS, AND YOUR CHOICE OF BEANS OR PLANT-BASED SAUSAGE.
TOSS INGREDIENTS WITH OLIVE OIL AND SEASONINGS. ROAST AT 400°F FOR 25–30 MINUTES, STIRRING HALFWAY.

GREEN POWER SMOOTHIE
KALE, FROZEN MANGO OR PINEAPPLE, BANANA, ALMOND MILK, CHIA OR FLAX SEEDS
ADD A SCOOP OF NUT BUTTER AND BLEND ALL INGREDIENTS ABOVE. BLEND UNTIL SMOOTH.

BREAKFAST QUICHE
EGGS, GREEN PEPPERS, RED ONION, SPINACH, CHOICE OF BREAKFAST MEAT (BEEF/TURKEY/CHICKEN BREAKFAST SAUSAGE). SHARP CHEDDAR CHEESE.COTTAGE CHEESE
MIX ALL INGREDIENTS TOGETHER, POUR INTO A GREASED BAKING DISH, AND BAKE AT 375°F FOR 30–35 MINUTES UNTIL SET; COOL SLIGHTLY AND CUT INTO PORTIONS.

IFTAR RECIPES

SAY: "I INTEND TO BREAK THE FAST FOR THIS DAY IN ORDER TO PERFORM MY DUTY TOWARDS ALLAH IN THE MONTH OF RAMADAN OF THE PRESENT YEAR."

ONE POT CHICKEN AND RICE

CHICKEN PORTIONS, GREEN PEPPER, RED PEPPER, ONION, CARROT, LONG GRAIN RICE, CHICKEN STOCK

SEASON AND SEAR CHICKEN UNTIL GOLDEN. SAUTÉ ONIONS AND GARLIC, ADD RICE, SPICES, AND BROTH ACCORDING TO THE WATER-TO-RICE RATIO, RETURN CHICKEN, COVER, AND SIMMER UNTIL TENDER—FLAVORFUL, FLUFFY, AND ALL IN ONE PAN.

SPAGHETTI

GROUND MEAT OF CHOICE, RED PEPPERS, ONIONS, BELL PEPPERS, YOUR SPAGHETTI SAUCE OF CHOICE, THIN SPAGHETTI

SAUTÉ PEPPERS AND ONIONS, ADD YOUR CHOICE OF MEAT, AND COOK UNTIL BROWNED. STIR IN PASTA SAUCE FOR A FEW MINUTES, THEN SERVE OVER THIN SPAGHETTI.

TURKEY MEATLOAF + MASHED POTATOES

GROUND TURKEY, GREEN PEPPERS, RED ONION, EGGS, ONION SOUP MIX, ITALIAN BREAD CRUMBS, SWEET BABY RAYS BBQ SAUCE, FIRE ROASTED DICED TOMATOES, RED POTATOES, BUTTER, HEAVY CREAM, SALT & PEPPER

MIX ALL INGREDIENTS TOGETHER, POUR INTO A GREASED BAKING DISH, AND BAKE AT 375°F FOR 30–35 MINUTES UNTIL SET; COOL SLIGHTLY AND CUT INTO PORTIONS. BOIL PEELED POTATOES UNTIL FORK-TENDER, DRAIN, THEN MASH WITH BUTTER, WARM MILK, SALT, AND PEPPER UNTIL SMOOTH AND CREAMY.

IFTAR RECIPES

SAY: "I INTEND TO BREAK THE FAST FOR THIS DAY IN ORDER TO PERFORM MY DUTY TOWARDS ALLAH IN THE MONTH OF RAMADAN OF THE PRESENT YEAR."

CREAMY TUSCAN GNOCCHI (VEGETARIAN)
BUTTER, GARLIC, HEAVY CREAM, CHICKEN OR VEGGIE BROTH, POTATO GNOCCHI UNCOOKED, SUN-DRIED TOMATOES GRATED PARMESAN CHEESE, BABY SPINACH.

SAUTÉ BUTTER AND GARLIC, THEN ADD CREAM AND BROTH. STIR IN UNCOOKED GNOCCHI, SUN-DRIED TOMATOES, PARMESAN, AND SPINACH. COOK UNTIL CREAMY AND GNOCCHI ARE TENDER.

HONEY GLAZED SALMON BOWL
SALMON, SOY SAUCE, GINGER, BROWN SUGAR, ORANGE JUICE, HONEY, CUCUMBER, AVOCADO, BASMATI RICE

MARINATE SALMON IN SOY, GINGER, BROWN SUGAR, AND ORANGE JUICE FOR 30 MINUTES, THEN COOK UNTIL GLAZED. SERVE OVER BASMATI RICE WITH RED ONION, CUCUMBER, AVOCADO, AND A DRIZZLE OF YUM YUM SAUCE.

CHICKEN PANINI & KETTLE CHIPS
ROTISSERIE CHICKEN, FOACCIA, CHIPOTLE MAYO, SPINACH, RED ONION, PLUM TOMATO, QUESADILLA CHEESE

BROWN BREAD ON BOTH SIDES, SPREAD MAYO ON INSIDE OF BREAD, LAYER WITH CHEESE, CHICKEN, TOMATOES, ONIONS AND SPINACH. GRILL ON BOTH SIDES AND SERVE WITH KETTLE CHIPS.

Surah (سورة): _____ Verse: _____

Translation

Reflection

Vocabulary

Intention

Surah (سورة): ____ Verse: ____

Translation

Reflection

Vocabulary

Intention

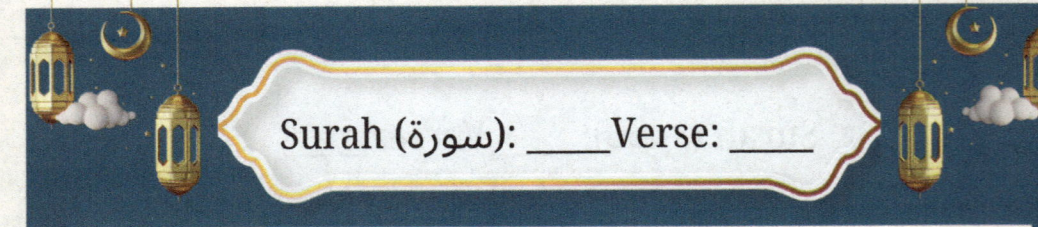

Surah (سورة): ____ Verse: ____

Translation

Reflection

Vocabulary

Intention

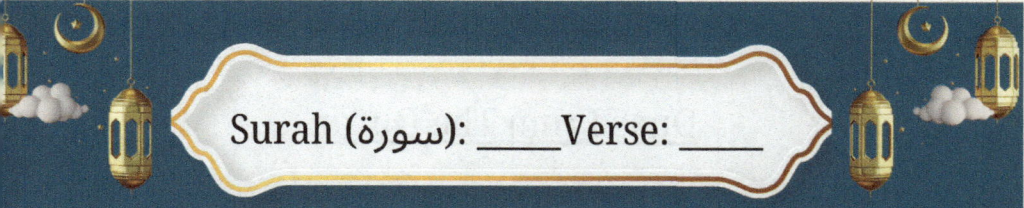

Surah (سورة): _____ Verse: _____

Translation

Reflection

Vocabulary

Intention

Duas From The Quran

Duas From The Quran

Duas From The Quran

Duas From The Quran

NOTES:

_____
_____
_____
_____
_____
_____
_____
_____
_____

NOTES:

NOTES:

_____
_____
_____
_____
_____
_____
_____
_____
_____

NOTES:

NOTES:

_____
_____
_____
_____
_____
_____
_____
_____
_____
_____

RAMADAN MADE EASY

BY: NAEEMAH S. CARSTON

FAITH, FAMILY, LEGACY

In this 3rd Edition of Ramadan Made Easy, author Naeemah S. Carston brings together the spiritual and the personal through guided reflections, worship trackers, family prompts, and heartfelt reminders that make each day of Ramadan purposeful and rooted in love.

WHAT'S INSIDE:

- Weekly reflection pages for prayer, gratitude, and self-accountability
- Family journaling prompts to help create new Ramadan traditions
- Legacy pages for elders and pioneers to share memories of past Ramadans
- Beautifully illustrated duas with QR codes linking to audio recitations by Naeemah's grandfather — a timeless connection to faith through voice
- Tips for building lasting habits beyond Eid

More than a planner or journal, this is a keepsake — a bridge between faith, family, and legacy designed to be opened year after year.
May your Ramadan be easy, intentional, and everlasting.

BIBLIOGRAPHY:

D. Karim, personal communication, January 1, 2024

Karim, Imam Darnell. Understanding Ramadan and Eid. Digital Publishing of Florida, Incorporated, 2020, pp. 6–30.

On The Spelling of G-d

"We are not the first to make this change. To recognize the word dog in reverse reading of the Name is distasteful. Many Jews agree. We favor such Jewish sentiments and share their concern."

-Imam W. Deen Mohammed

Oh, you who believe! Fasting is prescribed to you as it was prescribed to those before you, that you may learn piety and righteousness" [Qur'an,2:183]

"The month of Ramadan [is that] in which was revealed the Qur'an, a guidance for the people and clear proofs of guidance and criterion. So whoever sights [th`e new moon of] the month, let him fast it; and whoever is ill or on a journey – then an equal number of other days. Allah intends for you ease and does not intend for you hardship and [wants] for you to complete the period and to glorify Allah for that [to] which He has guided you, and perhaps you will be grateful." (Qur'an:,21:85)

"The Messenger of Allah (SWT) said: He who gives food for a fasting person to break his fast, he will receive the same reward as him, except that nothing will be reduced from the fasting person reward." [Ahmad, at-Tirmidhee, Ibn Maajah, Ibn Hibbaan, Saheeh]."

"Allah has made Laylat al-Qadr in this month, which is better than a thousand months, as Allah says…The Night of Al-Qadr is better than a thousand months. Therein descend the angels and the Rooh [Jibreel (Gabriel)] by Allah's Permission with all Decrees, there is peace until the appearance of dawn." — Al-Qadar 97:1-5

Made in the USA
Coppell, TX
20 February 2026

71960439R00056